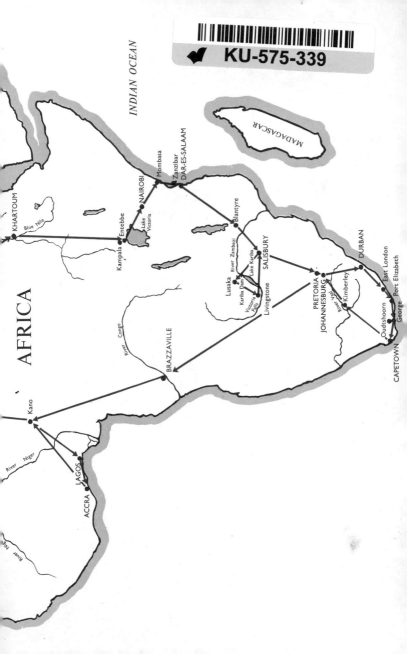

Series 587

FLIGHT FIVE:
AFRICA

by
DAVID SCOTT DANIELL

with illustrations by
JACK MATTHEW

Publishers : Wills & Hepworth Ltd., Loughborough

First Published 1961　　　　©　　　　*Printed in England*

Flight Five: AFRICA

One morning, soon after the sun had risen, an Arab in the Sahara Desert looked up into the sky. He screwed up his eyes against the glare of the sun and watched an air-liner far above him, so high that it looked as small as a tiny toy, silver in the sunlight. The Arab watched it for a few moments and then turned his attention to his camel. It was the leader of a long line, all loaded with bundles and sacks, plodding patiently along an age-old caravan route across the Sahara Desert to Timbuctoo.

The air-liner was a B.O.A.C. Comet 4, flying south into Africa at five-hundred miles an hour at a height of eight miles. Most of the sixty-three passengers were asleep, lulled by the smooth flight and the luxurious seats which tilted back to make beds. Among the passengers were two children, Alison and John, who were flying to Africa with their father.

Alison woke up and looked out of the port-hole. She shook the arm of her young brother.

" John, John! " she said excitedly, " wake up. It's morning and there's the Sahara Desert below us! "

John opened his eyes, yawned, scratched his head and looked out at the newly risen sun, and at the empty waste far below.

An hour later the air-liner dipped lower and lower as it prepared to land at Khartoum, the capital of the Sudan. They saw the famous River Nile, the white buildings and the pretty gardens.

" Look down there, Alison," John said, " on that road. See? Soldiers, riding on camels! Aren't they smart? "

" The Sudanese are very fine soldiers," said Daddy. " They were raised and trained by the British. Here we are in Khartoum, the first stop on our travels around Africa."

4

Alison and John spent several days in Khartoum, where Daddy had some business calls to make. They saw the Blue Nile, and they explored the city with its streets and squares of white buildings, its gardens and groves of coconut trees. Near the Nile all was fertile, but away from it was the barren desert.

Daddy told them the story of General Gordon, who was killed in Khartoum in 1885 after bravely withstanding a siege of more than ten months. John wrote a lot of facts in his notebook and Alison made some drawings of the native boats on the Nile, the grave and dignified Sudanese, and, of course, the camels.

From Khartoum they flew a thousand miles south to Uganda. They landed at Entebbe, on the northern shore of Lake Victoria, and motored to nearby Kampala, where Daddy had booked rooms in a hotel. The rooms had electric fans to keep them cool, and there were nets on frames over the beds to keep the mosquitoes out at night. The hotel was staffed by cheerful, smiling Africans.

They went for a trip on Lake Victoria and Alison, who had the guide-book, said, " Lake Victoria is the largest lake in Africa; half the size of England."

" And it was named after Queen Victoria," said John, " by J. H. Speke, the Englishman who discovered it."

" Here's another fact for you," Daddy said. " Lake Victoria is the source of the mighty River Nile, which flows northwards for nearly four-thousand miles through the Sudan and Egypt to the Mediterranean."

They had the good fortune to see a canoe regatta on the lake. The Africans paddled their canoes furiously as they raced, shouting and singing. It was very exciting.

6

One day Daddy took them for a drive into the country from Kampala. " Well, John," he said, " what do you know about Uganda? "

John opened his notebook. " Uganda is bigger than Great Britain," he said, " and it lies astride the Equator. To the south is Lake Victoria, to the west are the Mountains of the Moon, and to the east is Mount Elgon. But Daddy, if Uganda is on the equator, why isn't it terribly hot? It was hotter in Khartoum."

" D'you know the answer to that, Alison? " Daddy asked.

" I think so. It's because Uganda is on a high plateau, so it's only as hot as a good summer's day at home. And because of its lakes and rivers, much of it is green and fertile."

" Good. And what about crops, John? "

" Oh, cotton, Daddy, and coffee, are the main ones. Also cattle and farming of all kinds. And there are lots and lots of wild animals."

" Wild animals aren't a crop," Alison said.

" No, but they're jolly nice," John replied, " and in Uganda they've got elephants, buffalos, hippo's, rhino's, crocodiles, cheetahs, gorillas, zebras, giraffes, leopards—and lions! "

" It's like a zoological gardens turned loose," Daddy observed.

" Daddy, can we see some wild animals, please? " Alison asked in her nicest tone of voice.

" We'll see plenty before we leave Africa. But look, here's a village. I want you to see an African school. In 1900 there wasn't a school in Uganda. Now more than a million African children go to school. Let's stop and go up quietly and peep in at a window."

As they got near the school they heard the busy noise of the class-room. They looked in and watched for a few minutes.

" It's just the same as school at home," John whispered.

When the time came, neither Alison nor John wanted to leave Uganda; but since Daddy was travelling right round Africa they couldn't stay long in any one place. The next journey was a flight of three-hundred miles eastwards to Nairobi, the capital of Kenya, Uganda's neighbour.

A friend of Daddy's met them at the airport and drove them to his farm, where they were to spend a few days.

" Kenya looks just like Uganda," Alison said as they drove through the rich, green countryside.

" This part of Kenya is called the Central Highlands," Mr. Wells told her. " It's all very fertile farming land. But much of Kenya is more like desert."

" It was all wild country here once," Daddy explained, " until Europeans, mostly British people, settled."

" That's true," said Mr. Wells, " and not only did we cultivate the land and farm it, but we experimented to find out which varieties of seeds and plants grew best in this soil and climate."

" What do they grow in Kenya, sir? " John asked, his pencil and notebook ready.

" Oh, nearly everything. Wheat and maize, cotton, of course, and coffee. We send coffee all over the world. You've seen our cattle, and sheep and pigs, the same as on an English farm. And we grow tea, and sisal—for making rope and other things—and pineapples."

Mr. and Mrs. Wells and their three children lived in a splendid house with modern farm-buildings around it. It was a fine open-air life, and they had horses and ponies. The farm workers were Africans, who were very clever with the machinery.

Alison and John had a wonderful time on the farm in Kenya. Mr. Wells' children took them riding on ponies, they went fishing in the river and they explored it in a canoe. One hot day John suggested a swim, but Jimmy Wells looked round, laughed, and pointed to what appeared to be an old tree-trunk floating near the river bank.

" Look closer at that, John! " he said.

John looked, and then he saw what Jimmy meant. It wasn't a tree trunk at all ; it was an enormous crocodile! It opened its eyes, stared greedily at John, and then opened its mouth in a huge yawn, which showed an alarming array of vicious teeth.

" I see what you mean! " John said, paddling hard.

" Never mind," Jimmy said, " I know a safe place where we can swim."

One day Mr. Wells very kindly took them all for a long drive to one of the many Game Reserves in East Africa. In these Reserves the wild animals are protected and live their lives safe from the guns and traps of men.

Inside the Reserve the country was wild and rugged. Mr. Wells drove very slowly along the tracks and pointed out the interesting animals and birds. They saw an old rhino lumbering along happily, taking no notice of the motor car.

Mr. Wells took them to a special place he knew by a river and there they waited and watched. First a hippopotamus came, wallowing lazily in the river. Then a marabou stork and then, a wonderful sight, a family of African elephants. They strolled down to the river, their enormous ears flapping and their trunks waving from side to side. Father elephant came first, then mother elephant, and then a darling tubby little chap— the baby elephant.

Long before Alison and John were ready to go it was time to say good-bye to their friends on the Kenya farm, and to set off on the next stage of their African journey. This was a flight of three-hundred miles from Nairobi to Mombasa.

Mombasa is on the Indian Ocean, and it is the largest port in East Africa. It is built on a coral island, joined to the mainland by a road and rail causeway. Alison and John found the same wide streets and handsome white buildings as at Kampala and Nairobi, but there were also a number of picturesque old buildings, built more than two-hundred years ago, when Mombasa belonged to the Portuguese and Arabs.

They went to the docks, and watched tall cranes loading cargo into ships, to be taken all over the world. Hundreds of sacks of coffee were being loaded into the holds of a ship bound for England.

They were standing where they had a general view of the docks when Alison pointed out to sea. " Look, Daddy! A lovely old-fashioned sailing ship is coming in! "

" She is an Arab dhow," said Daddy, "and probably very much the same as the ships the Arab traders used when they came here two-thousand years ago! "

" Two-*thousand* years ago! " John said, astonished.

" Yes, John. The towns we have seen so far in Africa are all brand new, but Mombasa has a very long history as a port. There is evidence that the ancient Egyptians traded here, oh, five-thousand years ago. The ancient Greeks and the Phœnicians came, too, in their time, and for centuries it was used by the Arab traders."

14

They spent an enjoyable week in Mombasa, and often swam in the warm Indian ocean. Once when they were lying on a beach after a swim, John asked Daddy to tell them some more about Mombasa in the old days.

" Well, John, as I told you, the Arabs traded here for centuries. Then the Portuguese explorer Vasco da Gama came here in 1498, and for two centuries there was incessant fighting between the Portuguese and the Arabs. It was a valuable port, you see, because of the slave trade."

" Slaves? " Alison said. " What slaves? "

" African slaves. People used to go inland, round up a lot of Africans, and ship them away to be sold as slaves."

" How horrible! " said John.

" It was, John. That's where we came in first. Britain took a stand against slavery in the eighteenth century, and other countries followed suit. The British came here to stop the slave trade, and eventually we took over East Africa. Now the Africans share in the Government, and are being prepared to govern their countries themselves."

Daddy hired a car and took them inland to get a good view of the famous Mount Kilimanjaro, the highest mountain in Africa, over 19,000 feet. It is in Tanganyika, just over the border from Kenya. It was a magnificent spectacle with its great round dome capped with snow, like sugar on a plum pudding, although it is so near the equator. They watched some zebras and some giraffes, which always look taller than you expect, and some rather comical ostriches.

The next stage in their journey was south from Mombasa to Dar-es-Salaam, another port, and the capital of Tanganyika. In the lounge of their hotel John studied his notebook.

" Daddy," he said, " Alison has drawn a map of Africa in the back of my notebook.* Would you please put in the places we've been to so far? "

" Give me your pencil," Daddy said. " I'll do the best I can. Our first stop was Khartoum, the capital of the Sudan, here. Then we flew south to Entebbe, on Lake Victoria, and stayed at Kampala, the capital of Uganda. Next we flew into Kenya, to Nairobi, here, and went to stay with the Wells' family, about here. Then we flew to Mombasa, still in Kenya, and we saw Mount Kilimanjaro, just inside Tanganyika. Now we are here, at Dar-es-Salaam."

" I suppose," said Alison, thoughtfully, " that Uganda, Kenya and Tanganyika make up British East Africa, don't they? "

" Yes, and it's a total area nearly eight times the size of Great Britain, or a quarter of the United States of America. But we mustn't forget these two islands," and Daddy pointed to the map. " They're the Protectorate of Zanzibar, and they're part of British East Africa."

" What a lovely name," said John. " Zanzibar! "

" It's a wonderful place," Daddy said, " and to-morrow we're going there."

Zanzibar was indeed a wonderful place, full of ancient, narrow streets. The people were mostly Arabs, wearing flowing robes and head-cloths, or turbans. It was an exciting, mysterious place, and it seemed quite natural that the most important product of Zanzibar should be a spice—cloves.

*You can see the map in John's notebook opposite page 50.

When Daddy had finished his business in Dar-es-Salaam they flew south-west into Africa, calling at the capitals of the three countries of the Federation of Rhodesia and Nyasaland. They flew first to Blantyre in Nyasaland, on to Salisbury in Southern Rhodesia, then to Lusaka in Northern Rhodesia. Finally they went to Livingstone.

As soon as they were settled in their hotel in the pretty little town, Daddy took them off to see the famous Victoria Falls. They heard their roar as they drew near, like continuous thunder, and then they saw the spray, sparkling like diamonds high in the bright sunshine.

The Falls were an awe-inspiring sight. The mighty Zambezi River is more than a mile wide at the Falls, and the tremendous volume of water cascades over the edge, a sheer drop of three-hundred-and-four feet.

" The Africans call them *Mosi-oa-Tunya*," said Daddy, " 'the smoke that sounds'."

" The smoke is the *spray*! " Alison added. " It's like *thunder*! "

" Doctor Livingstone was the first white man to see the Victoria Falls," Daddy went on. " It was a hundred years ago. He named them after Queen Victoria."

" Wasn't Dr. Livingstone the famous missionary, Daddy? " asked John.

" Yes, John. He was a missionary, a doctor and a very brave explorer as well. He travelled right through the heart of Africa, the first white man to do so. He made very careful maps, healed the sick, made friends with the Africans, who were all savages then, and taught Christianity. Doctor Livingstone was a great and wonderful man, and the town we are staying in is named in honour of his memory."

After a short stay at Livingstone, they flew back to Salisbury in Southern Rhodesia. They were having lunch in their hotel when Alison said, thoughtfully, " Daddy, is it true that Rhodesia is called after a British explorer ? "

" Not after an explorer, Alison," Daddy replied. " It is named after a very clever and far-sighted Englishman named Cecil Rhodes, who made a great fortune out of diamonds in South Africa. He saw what a rich country this was, so he made peace with the African chiefs and used his fortune and his energy to develop the country. That is why it is called Rhodesia. When he died in 1902, he was buried high in the Matopo Hills, near Bulawayo."

" What is the ' Copperbelt ' ? " Alison asked.

" That's a good question! Its the area away in the north, on the border with the Congo, where there are very rich copper mines. There are gold mines in Rhodesia, too, and they also grow tobacco and tea."

" Tell us about the Kariba Dam, Daddy," John said.

" Well, you'll see for yourselves to-morrow. The Kariba Dam is an astonishing engineering feat. Where the Zambezi runs from Lake Kariba they have built an enormous dam which stops the water and forms a great lake, a hundred-and-seventy-five miles long and twenty-five miles wide. You saw the force of falling water at the Victoria Falls; well the Kariba Dam is to harness the power of water to make it drive turbines, to make electricity. There are a number of these hydro-electric plants in Africa, providing power for all the new industries. But, as I said, you'll see for yourselves to-morrow when we go to the Kariba Dam."

" Well, you two," Daddy said, with a smile, " that's the end of one part of our journey around Africa." They were in an air-liner flying south from Salisbury to Johannesburg in the Transvaal.

" I've loved every minute of it," Alison said.

" Me too," John chimed in, " and·so far we've been to eight different places." He ticked them off on his fingers. " The Sudan, Uganda, Kenya, Tanganyika, Zanzibar, Nyasaland, Southern Rhodesia and Northern Rhodesia."

" Yes, but do you know where we *haven't* been?" Daddy said. " We've missed out some very important parts of Africa. You must put them in your map,* John; Ethiopia, and Egypt. Then, right in the middle of Africa, is the Congo; you must put that in. We flew over Mozambique on the way to Nyasaland and Rhodesia, but we haven't been there.

John wrote in the names carefully, and asked about the countries they were missing. Then he had to put his book away because the plane was going down to land at the Jan Smuts airport of Johannesburg. They had a further thirty-five mile drive to Pretoria to their hotel.

When they had unpacked their cases, Daddy took them for a stroll to see Pretoria, the seat of the government of South Africa. They saw at once that it was a beautiful place, with fine buildings, big parks and thousands of lovely trees, which Daddy said were jacarandas, for which Pretoria is famous. They went to see the Union Buildings, the headquarters of the Government of the Union of South Africa.

* *You can see the countries John put on his map opposite page* 50.

" Well," said Daddy suddenly at breakfast one morning, " what do you two young travellers think of Pretoria? "

Alison said, " Well, Daddy, it's a *dignified* city, and quiet and peaceful."

" That's not a bad description at all," Daddy said. " And Pretoria has every right to be dignified, because it is both the capital of the province, that's Transvaal, and the capital of the Union of South Africa, until 1961 a dominion of the British Commonwealth. But I've got some news for you, rather a special treat."

It was a treat indeed that Daddy announced. He had hired a car to take them on a two-hundred mile drive to the Kruger National Park, the famous wild life sanctuary. They were to live for two days in a thatched hut in a camp, and get up at dawn and motor very slowly through the two-hundred mile long game reserve.

It was as wonderful as they expected in their neat, little thatched hut, which they had to themselves. They were up before dawn, and drove off slowly in the first light, all alert and cameras ready. The Park was the home of leopards and cheetahs, elephants, giraffes and hippo's, crocodiles and baboons, and herds of zebras, buck and South African wildebeest—and, of course, lions.

Early on the first morning they saw some lions. John squeaked excitedly and pointed to a glade as Daddy stopped the car. There was a family of them; a proud and handsome lion, a wise looking lioness, and a light-hearted, carefree cub. They watched them with bated breath—and then the lion strolled over to the car and began to lick his reflection in the shiny hub of the wheel!

During their stay in the Kruger National Park, Alison and John saw so many wild animals and birds, large and small, that notebook and sketch-book were nearly filled and several spools of film were used. When the time came to go, they tidied their hut and drove away, waving good-bye to all the elephants, giraffes and baboons they saw.

At Johannesburg they went to the airport and set off on a four-hundred mile flight south-east to Durban, on the coast of Natal. Durban proved to be a seaside city of gleaming white buildings, with a golden beach, a long sea-front, and a fine harbour.

Durban and the many seaside resorts up and down the coast were very modern, but inland it was the reverse. A business friend of Daddy's, Mr. van Meeteren, took them for a long drive into Zululand, a rolling sunlit countryside north of Durban. Before long they saw some Zulu 'kraals'—round huts like beehives.

Mr. van Meeteren told them that the Zulus are the descendants of a proud warrior race. Now they live peaceably farming their land. The women work in the fields and look after the homes, the boys herd the cattle, and spend most of their time playing in the sunshine, while the men take it all easily. Daddy and John thought this an excellent arrangement, but Alison didn't agree!

They visited the kraal of a Zulu Mr. van Meeteren knew, and the Zulu family were delighted to receive visitors, and did all they could to make them feel at home. To please Alison and John, the father put on his warrior clothes and the mother her best head-dress.

The next step on their journey was south-west from Durban, a flight of four-hundred miles along the coast of South Africa. They landed at East London, a busy seaside town at the mouth of the river Buffalo. When they were bathing off the beach, Alison and John watched a great liner setting out on its voyage from the port; it was a lovely sight.

When Daddy took them for a drive inland they saw enormous pineapple plantations, with African women carrying large baskets of pineapples on their heads.

" You know," Alison observed, thoughtfully, " that's a jolly good way to carry things, like Africans do—on your head."

" It would give you a fine straight back if you always did it," Daddy said.

For a change they made the next stage of their journey by road. A drive of two-hundred miles through splendid scenery took them to Port Elizabeth, where they spent a few days. It was another seaside town, with beaches and promenades, and it was also another big port. In the country around Port Elizabeth they saw orange groves everywhere, and in the port oranges were being loaded into ships.

When they left Port Elizabeth they drove along the famous ' Garden Route '. It was a fine fast road all along the lovely coastline, past pretty little seaside villages and through giant forests. They stayed at a town called George, and Daddy drove them inland for an hour to Oudtshoorn, to see an ostrich farm.

They were taken around the farm and saw ostriches everywhere, grown ones and comical chicks. The ostriches seemed to be just as interested to watch the visitors as the visitors were interested—and amused—to watch them.

The drive from George, still along the ' Garden Route ', took them to Cape Town, the great city on the southern tip of Africa. As they drew near they all looked out for Table Mountain, the world famous landmark. John saw it first, and claimed the penny prize.

Daddy slowed down and pulled in to the side of the road. It was a wonderful sight; the blue sea, with a liner coming towards the port; the roofs of the town nestling round the bay, and behind it the flat-topped mountain.

" No wonder they call it *Table* Mountain! " Alison said.

When they explored Cape Town they found quaint, little old streets, and foreign-looking houses and churches huddled among the fine new buildings. Daddy took them up the mile-long avenue of oaks, most of them two-hundred-and-fifty years old, to see the Houses of Parliament.

" But, Daddy," John said, " you said Pretoria was the seat of Government of South Africa. I put it in my notebook."

" And you were quite right, but the Parliament of South Africa meets here, in Cape Town," Daddy explained.

Cape Town was a splendid place to stay in. Daddy told them some of its history, which John wrote down carefully in his book.

" Before the Suez Canal was made in Egypt," he wrote, " ships going to India from Europe had to sail round the Cape of Good Hope. It was discovered by Bartholomew Diaz, a Portuguese explorer, in 1486. Cape Town began when a Dutchman built a small town in 1652, where ships could call on the voyage to India. It became British in 1795. In 1910 South Africa became part of the British Commonwealth of Nations, until 1961."

One of Daddy's business friends in Cape Town invited Daddy and the two children to spend a few days with him on his farm in the country. When they drove up to the house they saw people picking grapes in the vineyards, to make South African wine. It was a big old-fashioned stone house, painted white.

" We're very lucky," Daddy said, " to be staying in an old Cape Dutch homestead."

" Why is it called a *Dutch* homestead? " Alison asked.

" Because it's built in the Dutch style," Daddy's friend explained. " You see, the Dutch lived in the Cape first. They were farmers and they built their homes like the houses in Holland. That was before the 'Great Trek', of course."

" What was the 'Great Trek', sir? " John asked.

" Oh, you can't be in South Africa without knowing about that," Daddy's friend said. " You see, when the Cape was given to Britain by treaty a hundred-and-fifty years ago, British settlers came out here to live. The Dutch farmers, or Boers as they were called, naturally resented the newcomers. There were quarrels between the Boers and the British for many reasons.

" So in 1836, the Boers decided to go away. They packed their possessions into their great lumbering ox wagons and set off, with their families and their cattle, to find new land.

" It was a great adventure. They drove their ox-wagons far away into unknown parts of South Africa, inhabited only by savage tribes and wild animals, and settled in what is now Natal, the Orange Free State and Transvaal, across the River Vaal. That was the 'Great Trek'."

" What adventures they must have had! " John said.

Alison and John thoroughly enjoyed themselves on the farm, and had a good rest after all their travelling. But it was soon time to set off again. They flew six-hundred miles north-east to Kimberley, the famous town on the borders of Cape Province and the Orange Free State.

At supper in their hotel, Daddy said, " You've seen what a fine, prosperous town Kimberley is. Well, in 1871 there was nothing here! Then one day a farmer noticed a child playing with a pretty stone, and that was the start of Kimberley, and of great wealth for South Africa."

" Was the stone a diamond, Daddy? " asked Alison.

" It was, Alison. Other diamonds were found and the news spread. Fortune hunters came from all over the world. A mining camp sprang up, a ramshackle place where living was harsh and tough. Some men were killed in fights, most of them lost the little money they had, but a few made immense fortunes. For deep in the ground by the River Vaal were the finest diamonds in the world. So the rich town of Kimberley was built. To-morrow I'll take you to see the diamond mines."

At the diamond mines they saw how the diamonds were obtained. The rock containing diamonds was blasted deep down in the earth. It was brought to the top, and treated in a complicated way so that the rock was washed, crushed and sifted, and eventually the precious diamonds were separated.

They saw the ' Big Hole '. It is the biggest man-made hole in the world, dating from the early days of mining. They admired the clever guard dogs, who are ever on the watch to catch and hold anyone who dares to try to steal any diamonds.

After a few days at Kimberley they flew to Johannesburg, where their visit to South Africa had begun. As they drove to their hotel through the busy, bustling streets, Daddy said, " Here's an interesting fact. The story of Johannesburg is like the story of Kimberley."

" Did they discover diamonds, Daddy? " Alison asked.

" No, not diamonds—gold. Seventy years ago it was all wild, until they discovered the richest gold reef in the world. Then it happened just as it did at Kimberley. Fortune seekers hurried here and a rough and lawless mining-camp was put up. Gradually order was restored, the mining was properly organised—and this great city of Johannesburg was born."

The next day they flew from sunny South Africa for one-thousand, seven-hundred miles north-westerly to Brazzaville, on the River Congo. It is near the equator and Alison and John found it exceedingly hot. A friend of Daddy's took them for a most exciting drive along a dusty road between the great river and the jungle, where everything grows in rank profusion.

The purpose of the drive was to visit a French friend of Daddy's. He was a missionary and doctor, and he had a little church and a small hospital in a village on the bank of the Congo. You can imagine how pleased he was to see Daddy and the children.

In the afternoon they all went to bed; it was too hot to do anything else but sleep. But in the evening everyone was very busy, and Alison and John watched the Africans who had travelled a long way to come to see the doctor.

Their two-day visit to the Mission station seemed much too short. It was such a happy place, with the Africans for ever singing and laughing. In church they sang the hymns with great gusto and enjoyment.

It was not only Daddy's missionary friend who stood and waved good-bye when they went away. The African nurses, and all the men, women and children from the village were all waving and smiling as well.

" Why does he live out here," Alison said, " so far from home and everyone? "

" Because he is a very good man, Alison," Daddy said, seriously. " He is happy helping the Africans, teaching them Christianity, and using his skill as a doctor to heal them. There are many like him in Africa, men and women who devote their lives to managing missions and hospitals. A hundred years ago Doctor Livingstone came to Africa for that reason, and ever since good people have followed his example."

They set off from Brazzaville on a flight of twelve-hundred miles to Kano in Northern Nigeria. As the air-liner came down they had a fine view of the domes and towers of the ancient city.

" Look," Alison said, clutching John's arm, " a line of camels with their Arabs! "

" That's a caravan," said John. " See how the camels are loaded."

" Caravans like that have been coming to Kano for a thousand years," Daddy said. " They come from all over Africa, with goods to barter in the famous market of Kano."

They found that Kano was in two distinct parts; the ancient walled city and the modern city, with new buildings and an up-to-date look. Daddy said that Kano would be a good place to buy their presents to take home, so he took them to the market.

It was a wonderful sight. Everything you could think of was on sale, and there were many things made by Nigerian and other African craftsmen. People strolled about, looking at the merchants' wares, while some argued about the price. Daddy explained that you weren't expected to pay the price you were asked; people enjoyed arguing about it.

They discussed the presents they were going to buy at great length, and at last they made up their minds. For Mummy they bought a very colourful woven cloth to be used as a bedspread. They bought a gay leather bag with tassels for their young sister Mary, and for little Peter, three jolly little ebony elephants with ivory tusks. Daddy bought Alison and John a little elephant each as well.

After supper in the hotel, Daddy got out his map; and John got ready to add to the map* in his notebook.

" Here's Nigeria," Daddy said, pointing to it on the map, " and here's the great River Niger, which gives the country its name. To be correct, it is ' The Federation of Nigeria'. The capital is Lagos, down there on the mouth of the Niger. That's where we are going to-morrow."

Alison watched—and advised—John as he carefully put Nigeria in his map.

* *You can see John's map opposite page* 50.

When Daddy finished his business in Kano they flew south, right down Nigeria, to Lagos. Here was another city to look at, similar to the other modern African towns they had seen, yet with its own particular character. They wandered round the port, and noticed that, as always in Africa, people sang cheerfully as they worked.

Three days later they were off again, flying westwards along the coast to Accra, the capital of Ghana. As they drove to their hotel Daddy told them that it had been called the Gold Coast until 1957, when it became an independent state within the British Commonwealth, and changed its name to Ghana.

" Was it called the Gold Coast because there was gold here ? " Alison asked.

" Yes indeed, and there still is gold, but not in such quantities as in South Africa. And diamonds, too. Nowadays the wealth of Ghana comes mainly from cocoa, which is shipped all over the world to make chocolate."

Alison and John were so interested in the subject of chocolate that Daddy arranged for a friend of his to take them to visit an African farmer who grew cocoa.

They found the farmer in his cocoa plantation cutting the cocoa pods off the trunks of the trees. Two children followed picking them up. They carried the pods to a place where the rest of the family were sitting on the ground splitting open the pods and scooping out the white, pulpy cocoa beans.

Daddy's friend explained that the piles of beans were covered with leaves for a few days, until they turned chocolate colour. They were put into sacks when they were dry, then taken to market and sold.

As they drove away from the farm Daddy's friend said, " All the cocoa is grown by African farmers. It provides a good living for thousands of them."

" I'll always think of them when I eat chocolate," Alison said.

" What about coconuts? " John asked suddenly.

" Coconuts don't give you cocoa," Daddy said. " Coconuts are picked to obtain copra, for coconut oil. It's used for making soap, among other things."

" You should see the African boys climb up the tall palm trees to pick the coconuts—they're wonderfully nimble." Daddy's friend added.

They stopped in a village, where Alison made a sketch and John talked to a little boy with a parrot. They were friendly people in the village. Some wore European clothes, some the gaily coloured ' cloths,' and the very young children didn't bother to wear any clothes at all.

An elderly man was carving wooden stools, using his feet as extra hands to hold the wood. John was delighted to see a solemn little boy come home from school carrying his homework and a bottle of ink on his head.

" It's such a sensible thing to do," Alison said, " and so is the way mothers carry their babies on their backs."

" A continuous piggy-back ride! " John added.

" Africa is a wonderful mixture of the old and new," Daddy said. " You see old crafts and customs, and the simplest way of life. Yet they have bicycles and radio sets, and that little boy with his books on his head may become a doctor or a lawyer, or a Member of the Ghana Parliament when he grows up."

On the drive back from the village Daddy's friend turned off the main road as they approached Accra.

" I'm going to show you something important," he said. " It has to do with that little fellow you saw with the book and an ink-bottle on his head—or perhaps it will, one of these days."

He turned up a wide avenue and pointed to a group of handsome new buildings at the end. " That is the University College of Ghana," he said. " We'll get out and have a look around."

They walked around the white buildings with red roofs, surrounded by beds of bright flowers. Young men stood about chatting, wearing blue gowns. Daddy's friend explained the various buildings of the University.

" Did you mean that the little boy we saw might come here, sir ? " John asked.

" If he works hard, yes. Once, and not long ago, he would have lived in his village all his life, and not even learnt to read and write. Now he can go to a grammar school when he is old enough, and then to the University, and, as your Father said, he can become a doctor, lawyer, engineer or a school teacher."

" It's the same all over Africa," said Daddy. " Africa is growing up. People still believe in witch doctors and magic, and millions can't read or write. But they are eager for education. And in all the countries which have been under British control they are being given their independence as soon as they are able to manage their own affairs."

" I should think that chap of ours with the book on his head will be a jolly good Prime Minister of Ghana some day," said John.

When the time came to go home Alison and John were sorry to say good-bye to Africa. Their air-liner left Accra at four o'clock in the afternoon on the three-thousand, seven-hundred mile journey to London. There were two stops of three-quarters of an hour at Kano and Rome, and they were due in London at eight o'clock the next morning.

When the stewards had served afternoon tea, John took out his notebook and opened it at his map.

" We've been to eleven countries," he said, and he pointed to them on the map. " The Sudan; Uganda, Kenya and Tanganyika; Nyasaland, Southern and Northern Rhodesia; South Africa, the Congo, Nigeria and Ghana."

" You've forgotten one," Alison said. " Zanzibar, so that makes twelve! "

" Have you noticed," said Daddy, " that they've all been British except the Sudan and the Congo? And we haven't seen anything like all of Africa. Look, over here to the east of your map we missed Ethiopia, Eritrea, British Somaliland and Somalia; and Mozambique and Madagascar."

" And we missed these places in the north, too," John said. " Morocco, Algeria, Tunisia, Libya and Egypt."

" Think of all the enormous jungle we missed," Alison said with a sigh, " and the great Sahara Desert! But let's be thankful for all we have seen. And I like Africa, and the Africans! "

" So do I," John added, " and I like the wild animals too.

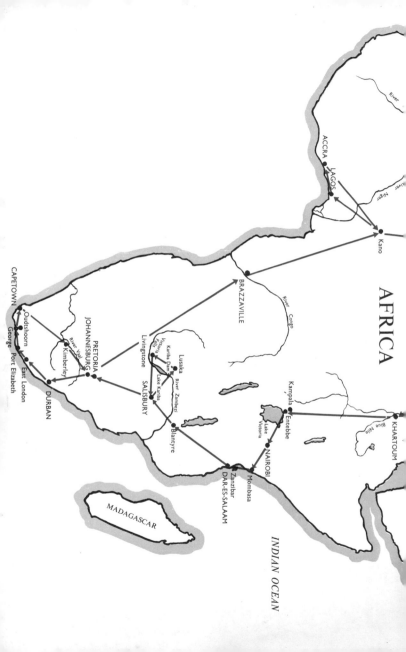